PIANO/VOCAL/CHORDS

100 YEARS OF POPULAR

2000

CW00350728

Series Editor:
Carol Cuellar

Editorial and Production:
Artemis Music Limited

Design and Production:
JPCreativeGroup.com

Published 2003

International
MUSIC
Publications

International Music Publications Limited
Griffin House 161 Hammersmith Road London W6 8BS England

CONTENTS

TITLE	PAGE

2000

The shiny "2000 hats" were discarded. The T-shirts with the "1999 Game Over" slogan were already tucked away as souvenirs; so was the "Millennium Babe" lipstick. Sitting at our computers on the morning of January 1, 2000, we breathed a collective sigh of relief.

Planes had not fallen out of the sky, the financial markets did not dissolve into chaos, security alarms did not wail mindlessly throughout London. The Y2K bug had proven to be a harmless gnat, rather than the swarm of killer bees that many had predicted.

Still, all of the talk about Y2K and its potential for wreaking havoc on the orderly flow of daily life had tapped into a vague, but deep, sense of anxiety, reminding us that we did indeed live in a delicately balanced world; a world in which comforting routines and familiar reassurances could come crashing down in an instant as a result of distant, mysterious events.

This would, of course, happen early in the new millennium, though not as the result of a glitch in computer software . . .

One need not elaborate on September 11, 2001 with identifying words like "World Trade Tower", or "Al-Qaeda". The date by itself is enough.

Few dates in history have possessed its evocative power, and fewer still have wrought so many changes in such short order. In the eighteen months that followed the attacks on New York and Washington, the UK and the US waged wars in Afghanistan and then Iraq; millions took to the streets in protest; and old alliances were suddenly strained to breaking point.

As so often happens during times when history looms large, people of this era have bravely reaffirmed their individual identities by celebrating those intensely personal, wonderfully eccentric, and unfailingly human qualities that make them unique.

This spirit has been reflected in the music of the era. Whether it's a remake of a standard, or a new song written and recorded by a young sensation, the most memorable hits on the post-2000 charts resound with private, often idiosyncratic, voices that defy easy categorisation.

The personalisation of pop music was evident in the new decade even before 11 September 11. Awed and humbled by the passing of the millennium, musicians created works that reached the most private recesses of the heart and soul. It was as if these artists were intent on delivering a message to future generations: "We were here at this momentous time, and our music is one of the things that made us human".

Inspired by the sense of history that the millennium inevitably evoked, many artists paid homage to musical ideas from earlier eras while giving them a distinctive new 21st Century twist. Reggae genius Shaggy did this with "Angel", on his hit album *Hot Shot*. Based on the classic '60s hit "Angel Of The Morning", this song features an unforgettable funk guitar sample of Steve Miller's hit "The Joker".

The Irish boy band Westlife has a sound that is quite different than Shaggy's mix, but it, too, reached back into the past to create a catchy 21st Century version of a familiar standard. Westlife's cover of the Billy Joel song "Uptown Girl", which the group recorded for the Comic Relief Charity, became a No.1 hit in the UK. This marked the eighth time that a single by the group topped the charts.

Toploader, the Eastbourne, East Sussex-based quintet, also drew on retro influences. In February 2000, it released a cover of the 1973 hit "Dancing In The Moonlight". The group's gleeful recording of this energetic classic allowed it to break through the UK Top 20.

On August 20, 2000, Toploader became a part of history itself, when it performed as the opening act in the last concert at Wembley Stadium before it was rebuilt. Comprised of keyboardist/vocalist Joseph Washbourn, guitarists Dan Hipgrave and Julian Deane, bassist Matt Knight, and drummer Rob Green, Toploader emerged as one of the hottest acts in the years following 2000. The group's playful sound, reminiscent of '70s white soul party music, provided a welcome antidote to the stress and turbulence following September 11.

Dance and DJ music, which had been a vibrant form of musical expression in the previous decade, also gained new momentum in the post-millennium world, in part because both provided a welcome refuge from the events taking place beyond the club walls.

Sophie Ellis-Bextor became a major star in late 2000 when she appeared with Italian DJ Spiller on his disco house hit "Groovejet (If This Ain't Love)". Ellis-Bextor's lush voice worked perfectly over the deep grooves of the Italian's dance song, propelling it to the top of singles charts around the world. The popularity of the song was undoubtedly helped by the release of a video that paired the fine-boned, porcelain-skinned beauty from West London with the imposing 6'9" Venetian. Following her hit with Spiller, Ellis-Bextor went to the top of the charts on her own with songs like the club tune "Murder On The Dancefloor".

Another club diva, Sonique, embodied the personalised, independent spirit of the new century in songs like the rhythmic hit "I Put A Spell On You". Born Sonia Clarke, this charismatic Londoner was a runner, diver, and gymnast, before becoming a DJ and singer. Fusing a variety of musical influences into her work, Sonique has earned widespread acclaim, as evidenced by her Ivor Novello Award and Best British Female Brit Award.

Father, what did YOU do to mark the Millennium?

The growth of dance music also helped beautiful Australian Kylie Minogue stage a remarkable post-millennium comeback. Minogue was flying high on the UK charts in the late '80s and early '90s, releasing multiple No.1 hits and Top Ten tunes. Then her fortunes declined in 1994, when she began experimenting with a grungier sound.

Happily for the diva's legion of loyal fans, Minogue later re-emerged as a dance music star. Her 2001 hit, "Can't Get You Out Of My Head", written by former Mud guitarist Rob Davis and Cathy Dennis, topped the UK charts and broke into the US Top 10 as well. For good measure, the song won three Ivor Novello Awards.

Just as many music fans sought an escape from uncertain times on the dance floors, others took comfort in more reflective ballads and love songs. In the mid '90s, Dido was immersed in trip-hop music as a singer with Faithless, a techno-driven band led by her brother, the noted DJ Rollo. As the new millennium approached, Dido's musical interest took on a softer, more pensive bent. Her debut album, *No Angel*, produced by Rollo and Youth, featured "Thank You", a heartfelt song about love and friendship, which was written in honour of her long-time boyfriend. The song received widespread attention as part of the soundtrack for the film *Sliding Doors*. However, real notoriety came when the American rap star Eminem sampled it for the chorus of his hit "Stan".

Interest in "Thank You" soared as a result of the Eminem exposure. The song became a Top Five UK hit in early 2001, and sales of its album reached three million.

Richard Ashcroft is another alternative artist who developed a more mellow sound following the millennium. In the 1990s, Ashcroft became famous as the charismatic leader of the indie rock band The Verve. In the late '90s, he moved toward a more soul-searching sound. The warm vocals in songs like "Check The Meaning" make Ashcroft an ideal troubadour for these times.

It is fitting that an era that prized such deeply personal forms of music should also spawn an

outpouring of rich and vivid works of fantasy. What, after all, can be more "private" than to cut the ties that bind us to the real world and journey far into the wondrous realm of the imagination? *The Lord Of The Rings* and *Harry Potter* both guided millions of movie fans on just such fantastic journeys.

These modern fiction masterpieces were turned into wildly successful films in the early years of the new millennium. Released in December 2001, *The Lord Of The Rings: The Fellowship Of The Ring* was nominated for 13 Academy Awards and garnered over $860 million in worldwide revenues. The making of the first *Harry Potter* film was a news story unto itself. Some 16,000 British boys auditioned for the role of Harry in the film, which was made largely at the Leavesden Studios, a former Rolls Royce factory just off the M25 near Watford.

Audiences around the world were captivated by the compelling stories, stunning effects, and evocative musical scores of both films. In its own way, each creative work exerted a magical pull on the mind and spirit, reminding us that even in times of monumental world events, nothing can ever quell the power of the human imagination.

Ten Things That First Appeared In The 2000 Decade

1. **Segway human transporters.**
2. **Dog translating devices, Japan.**
3. **Breath strips, USA.**
4. **Lemon and ginger spiced ale.**
5. **Artificial liver.**
6. **Sex and the city flower rosettes on clothes.**
7. **Foam rubber microphones.**
8. **Invisibility coats, Japan.**
9. **Self-cleaning windows, USA.**
10. **Harry Potter on film.**

A WOMAN'S WORTH

Words and Music by ALICIA AUGELLO-COOK and ERIKA ROSE

© 2001 Lellow Productions, USA
EMI Music Publishing Ltd, London WC2H 0QY

ANGEL

Words and Music by ORVILLE BURRELL, RICARDO DUCENT,
NIGEL STAFF, SHAUN PIZZONIA, DAVE KELLY, CHIP TAYLOR,
STEVE MILLER, AHMET ERTEGUN and EDDIE CURTIS

© 2001 Livingsting Music, Greensleeves Publishing, Dave Kelly Music, EMI Blackwood Music Inc and Sailor Music, USA
EMI Songs Ltd, London WC2H 0QY and Windswept Pacific Music Ltd, London W6 9BD
[This song contains a sample from "Angel Of The Morning" by Taylor © EMI Blackwood Music Inc and "The Joker" by
Miller, Ertegun & Curtis © Windswept Music]

19

Verse 2:
You're a queen and that's how you should be treated
Though you never get the loving that you needed
Could have left, but I call and you heeded
Takin' a beatin', mission completed
Mama said that and I dissed the program
Not the type to mess around with your emotion
But the feeling that I have for you so strong
Been together so long and this could never be wrong.

ANYTHING IS POSSIBLE

Words and Music by CATHY DENNIS and CHRIS BRAIDE

© 2001 EMI Music Publishing Ltd, London WC2H 0QY and Warner/Chappell Music Ltd, London W6 8BS

24

CAN WE FIX IT

Words and Music by PAUL K JOYCE

© 2000 Hit Entertainment Plc
EMI Music Publishing Ltd, London WC2H 0QY and BBC Worldwide Music, London W12 0TT

CAN YOU DIG IT?

Words and Music by MARTIN COOGAN

© 1990 EMI Virgin Music Ltd, London WC2H 0QY

Some - one turned_ their light_ on._
But some - one turned_ our light_

CAN'T FIGHT THE MOONLIGHT

Words and Music by DIANE WARREN

© 2000 Realsongs, USA
EMI Music Publishing Ltd, London WC2H 0QY

CHECK THE MEANING

Words and Music by RICHARD ASHCROFT

1. When I'm

© 2002 EMI Music Publishing Ltd, London WC2H 0QY

CAN'T GET YOU OUT OF MY HEAD

Words and Music by CATHY DENNIS
and ROBERT DAVIS

© 2000 EMI Music Publishing Ltd, London WC2H 0QY and Universal/MCA Music Ltd, London W6 8JA

COME AWAY WITH ME

Words and Music by NORAH JONES

© 2002 Muthajones Music and EMI Blackwood Music Inc, USA
EMI Music Publishing Ltd, London WC2H 0QY

DIRRTY

Words and Music by DANA STINSON,
CHRISTINA AGUILERA, BALEWA MUHAMMAD,
JASPER CAMERON and REGGIE NOBLE

(Spoken:)Dirrty, filthy, nasty. Too dirrty to clean my act up.
If you ain't dirrty, you ain't here to party.

© 2002 Warner-Tamerlane Publishing Corp, Dayna's Day Publishing, Christina Aguilera Music, Jahque Joints,
Jasper Cameron Publishing Designee and Funky Noble Productions, USA
Warner/Chappell North America Ltd, London W6 8BS, Universal Music Publishing Ltd, London W6 8JA,
BMG Music Publishing Ltd, London SW6 3JW and Copyright Control

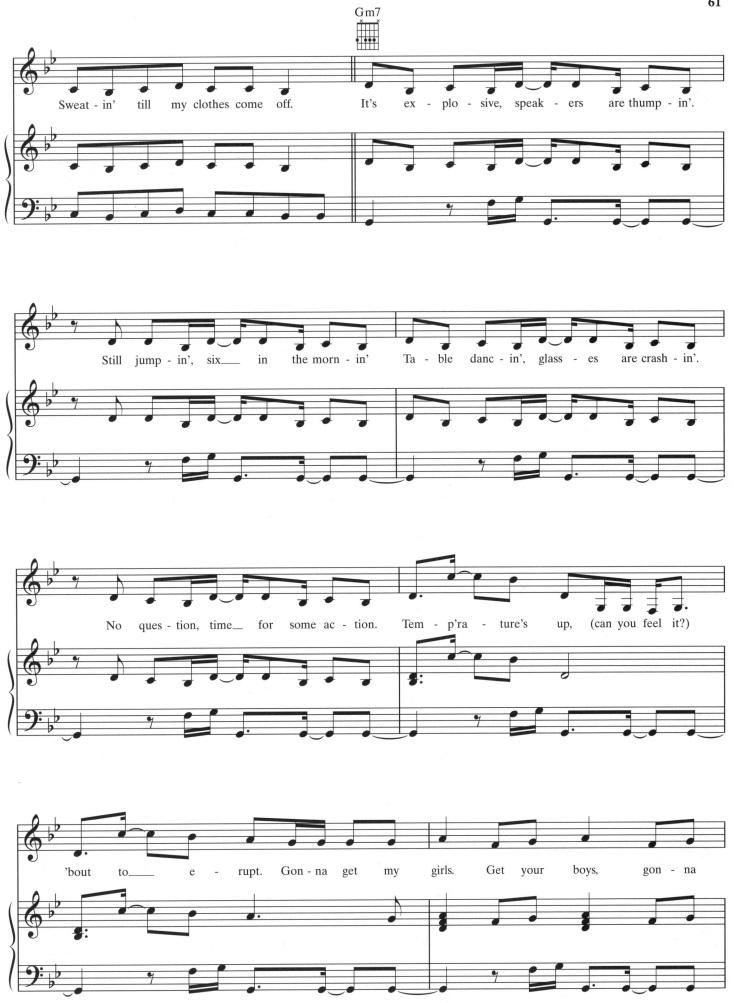

Chorus:

Verse 2:
Ah, heat is up, so ladies, fellas, drop your cups.
Body's hot from front to back.
Move your ass, I like that.
Tight hip-huggers, low, fo' sho'.
Shake a little somethin' on the floor.
I need that to get me off.
Sweatin' till my clothes come off.
Let's get up and cause a commotion.
We still goin', eight in the mornin'.
There's no stoppin', we keep it poppin'.
Hard rockin', everyone's talkin'.
Give all you got, just hit the spot.
Gonna get my girls, get your boys.
Gonna make some noise.
(To Chorus:)

COME UNDONE

Words and Music by ROBERT WILLIAMS, DANIEL PIERRE,
ASHLEY HAMILTON and PIERRE OTTESTAD

So un-im-pressed but so in awe, ___ such a saint ___ but such a whore. ___
So rock and roll ___ so cor-porate suit, ___ so damn ug - ly so damn cute. ___

© 2002 BMG Music Publishing Ltd, Cementhead BC Music, EMI April Music Inc, EMI Blackwood Music Inc and Copyright Control
BMG Music Publishing Ltd, London SW6 3JW, EMI Music Publishing Ltd, London WC2H 0QY and Copyright Control

COMPLICATED

Words and Music by LAUREN CHRISTY, DAVID ALSPACH,
GRAHAM EDWARDS and AVRIL LAVIGNE

© 2002 Rainbow Fish Music, Ferry Hill Songs, Mr Spock Music, Warner-Tamerlane Publishing Corp, USA
and Rondor Music (London) Ltd
Warner/Chappell North America Ltd, London W6 8BS and Rondor Music (London) Ltd, London W6 8JA

CORNER OF THE EARTH

Words and Music by JASON KAY and ROBERT HARRIS

© 2001 EMI Music Publishing Ltd, London WC2H 0QY

DANCING IN THE MOONLIGHT

Words and Music by SHERMAN KELLY

© 1970 EMI Catalogue Partnership, EMI U Catalog Inc, St Nathanson Music Ltd and EMI United Partnership Ltd, USA
Worldwide print rights controlled by Warner Bros Publications Inc/IMP Ltd

DILEMMA

Words and Music by KENNETH GAMBLE, BUNNY SIGLER,
CORNELL HAYNES and ANTOINE MACONE

© 2002 Warner-Tamerlane Publishing Corp, Jackie Frost Music, BMG Songs Inc, Suga Shack Music,
Universal Music Corp, USA and Copyright Control
Warner/Chappell North America Ltd, London W6 8BS, BMG Music Publishing Ltd, London SW6 3JW and Copyright Control
[This song contains a sample from "Love, Need And Want You" by Gamble & Sigler © Warner/Chappell North America Ltd]

Verse 2:
I see a lot and you look and I never say a word.
I know how niggaz start actin' trippin' out here about they girls.
And there's no way Nelly gon' fight over no dame, as you could see.
But I like your steez, your style, your whole demeanor.
The way you come through and holla and swoop me in his two-seater.
Now that's gangstah and I got special ways to thank ya.
Don't you forget it but, it ain't that easy for you to pack up and leave him.
But you and dirty got ties for different reasons.
I respect that and right before I turn to leave, she said,
"You don't know what you mean to me."
(To Chorus:)

DREAMER

Words and Music by MARTI FREDERIKSEN,
OZZY OSBOURNE and MICHAEL JONES

© 2001 Pearl White Music, Monowise Ltd and Somerset Songs Publishing Inc, USA
EMI Virgin Music Ltd, London WC2H 0QY and Copyright Control

yeah.

Guitar

D.%. al Coda

4. If

Coda

I'm just a dream - er___ who's search - ing for___ the way___ to - day.____ I'm just a dream - er,____

dream - ing my life____ a - way.____ Oh, yeah, yeah,

yeah.____

Verse 4:
If only we could all just find serenity
It would be nice if we all could live as one
When will all this anger, hate and bigotry
Be gone?

I'm just a dreamer *etc.*

FALLIN'

Words and Music by ALICIA AUGELLO-COOK

I keep on fall - in' in _____ (Vocal ad lib.) and

out of love with - a you. Some - times_ I

love you some - times you make me blue. Some - times I feel

© 2001 Lellow Productions, USA
EMI Music Publishing Ltd, London WC2H 0QY

DY-NA-MI-TEE

Words and Music by NIOMI DALEY, SALAAM REMI,
LENNIE HIBBERT and CLEMENT DODD

1. same lit-tle girl that grew up next door to you, went through all the things— a teen-age girl goes through.— Hang-in'
(Verses 2 & 3 see block lyric)

© 2002 EMI Music Publishing Ltd, Salaam Remi Music Inc, EMI April Music Inc and Jamrec Music
EMI Music Publishing Ltd, London WC2H 0QY and Copyright Jamrec Music

Verse 2:
I remember all the house parties that took place
Bein' in my bed upstairs and we could still feel the bass
And my cousins and my brothers we'd sit up all night
Listenin' to my family vibin' till the morning light.
Remember my first years of school, I was so innocent
I just wanted to learn, I never been so content
But the more that I learned I found a guidin' light
That showed me the need to fight.

And be Ms. Dynamitee *etc.*

Verse 3:
At thirteen I thought I was in love with this guy
Anytime I caught his eye I thought that I'd just die
Remember playin' class clown, I was just a disruptive fool
And the beatin' I got first time suspended from school.
Remember Sunday School and after go to Granma's for lunch
Macaroni, rice and peas, chicken and pineapple punch
Never had much, my mum, brother, sister and me
But love was enough to succeed.

To grow, Ms. Dynamitee *etc.*

FEEL

Words and Music by ROBERT WILLIAMS
and GUY CHAMBERS

© 2001 BMG Music Publishing Ltd and EMI Music Publishing Ltd
BMG Music Publishing Ltd, London SW6 3JW and EMI Music Publishing Ltd, London WC2H 0QY

GENIE IN A BOTTLE

Words and Music by PAM SHEYNE,
DAVID FRANK and STEVE KIPNER

© 1999 Appletree Songs Limited, Stephen A Kipner Music, Griff Griff Music and EMI April Music Inc, USA
Warner/Chappell Music Limited, London W6 8BS and EMI Music Publishing Limited, London WC2H 0QY

GROOVEJET
(IF THIS AIN'T LOVE)

Words and Music by CRISTIANO SPILLER,
SOPHIE ELLIS-BEXTOR, ROBERT DAVIS,
VINCENT MONTANA JR and RON WALKER

1. Hold-ing you clos-er, it's time that I told you ev-'ry-thing's going to be fine.
(2.) Shame comes to-mor-row, we beg, steal or bor-row to make all we can in the sun.

Know that you mean it and try to be-lieve it, take me one step at a time.
While we are mov-ing the mu-sic is sooth-ing, trou-bles we thought had be-gun. If— this ain't love.—

© 2000 EMI Music Publishing Ltd, London WC2H 0QY, Rondor Music (London) Ltd, London W6 8JA,
Universal/MCA Music Ltd, London W6 8JA and The International Music Network, London E4 6PD

Will you re - mem - ber— me,— boy?—   Re - mem - ber me,   boy,— will you—

— re - mem - ber?

3. Just for this life - time you can be my pas - time,   here are the rules of our—

HANDBAGS AND GLADRAGS

Words and Music by MIKE D'ABO

1. Ev-er see a blind man cross the road
2. Once I was a young man

try'n' to make the oth-er side?_____
and all I thought I had to do   was smile._____

© 1967 D'Abo Songs Ltd and EMI United Partnership Ltd, USA
Worldwide print rights controlled by Warner Bros. Publications Inc/IMP Ltd

132

HAVE YOU EVER

Words and Music by ANDREW FRAMPTON,
CATHY DENNIS and CHRISTOPHER BRAIDE

© 2001 EMI Music Publishing Ltd, London WC2H 0QY and Warner/Chappell Music Ltd, London W6 8BS

HERE WITH ME

Words and Music by DIDO ARMSTRONG,
PAUL STATHAM and PASCAL GABRIEL

© 1996 Warner/Chappell Music Ltd, London W6 8BS

140

# 140

HERO

Words and Music by ENRIQUE IGLESIAS,
PAUL BARRY and MARK TAYLOR

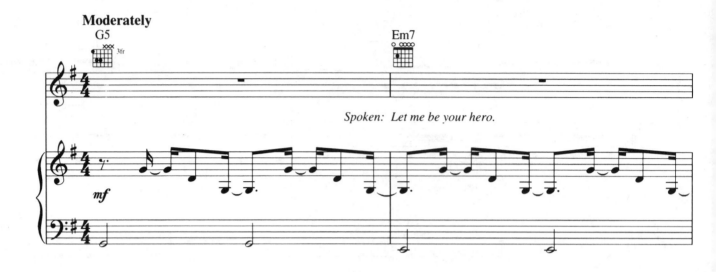

Spoken: Let me be your hero.

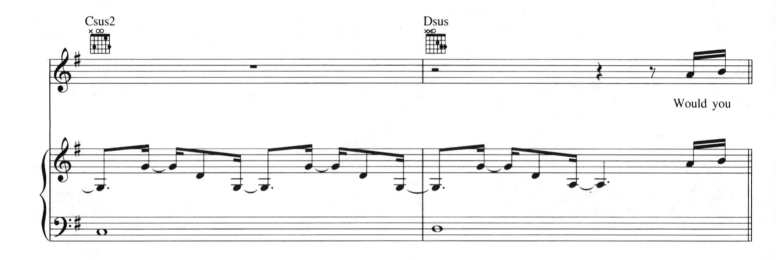

Would you

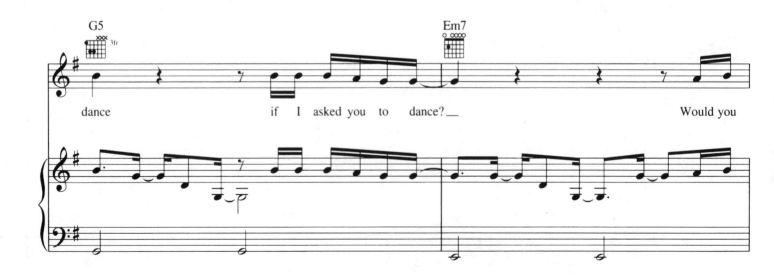

dance   if I asked you to   dance?   Would you

© 2001 Enrique Iglesias Music, USA, Rive Droite Music Ltd and Metrophonic Music Ltd
EMI Music Publishing Ltd, London WC2H 0QY, Rive Droite Music Ltd, Surrey KT1 4AE
and Metrophonic Music Ltd, London SE1 6DP

HOW YOU REMIND ME

Words and Music by CHAD KROEGER,
MICHAEL KROEGER, RYAN PEAKE and RYAN VIKEDAL

Drop D tuning: ⑥ = D

© 2001 Arm Your Dillo Publishing, Michael Kroeger Publishing Designee,
Ryan Peake Publishing Designee and Ryan Vikedal Publishing Designee, USA
Warner/Chappell North America Ltd, London W6 8BS

Verse 2:
It's not like you didn't know that.
I said I love you and swear I still do.
And it must have been so bad.
'Cause livin' with me must have damn near killed you.
This is how you remind me of what I really am.
This is how you remind me of what I really am.
(To Chorus:)

HEY BABY

Words and Music by BRUCE CHANNEL and MARGARET COBB

© 1962 EMI Catalogue Partnership, EMI Unart Catalog Inc and EMI United Partnership Ltd, USA
Worldwide print rights controlled by Warner Bros. Publications Inc/IMP Ltd

I LOVE ROCK 'N' ROLL

Words and Music by ALAN MERRILL and JAKE HOOKER

© 1975 RAK Publishing Ltd, London NW8 7BU

I PUT A SPELL ON YOU

Words and Music by JAY HAWKINS

© 1956 EMI Catalogue Partnership, EMI Unart Catalog Inc and EMI United Partnership Ltd, USA
Worldwide print rights controlled by Warner Bros. Publications Inc/IMP Ltd

I TURN TO YOU

Words and Music by MELANIE CHISHOLM,
RICK NOWELS and BILLY STEINBERG

1. When the world is dark - er than I can un - der - stand,

(Verse 2 see block lyrics)

© 1999 EMI Music Publishing (WP) Ltd, Jerk Awake, EMI April Music Inc and Future Furniture Music, USA
EMI Music Publishing Ltd, London WC2H 0QY

Verse 2:

When my insides are wracked with anxiety
You have the touch that will quiet me
You lift my spirit, you melt the ice
When I need inspiration, when I need advice.

I turn to you *etc.*

I WANT LOVE

Words by BERNIE TAUPIN
Music by ELTON JOHN

I want love_____ but it's im-pos-si-ble:_____

© 2001 Happenstance Music Ltd, Wretched Music Ltd and Big Pig Music Ltd, Netherlands
Warner/Chappell Artemis Music Ltd, London W6 8BS

I want love, won't break me down,— won't— brick me up,— won't fence me in.— I want a

love that don't mean a thing;— that's the love I want.— I— want— love.

Verse 3:
(Instrumental)
A man like me is dead in places
Other men feel liberated.

And I want love *etc.*

I'M LIKE A BIRD

Words and Music by NELLY FURTADO

© 2001 Nelstar Publishing
EMI Music Publishing Ltd, London WC2H 0QY

IT WASN'T ME

Words and Music by ORVILLE BURRELL, RICARDO DUCENT,
BRIAN THOMPSON, SHAUN PIZZONIA, SYLVESTER ALLEN,
HAROLD BROWN, MORRIS DICKERSON, LEROY JORDAN,
CHARLES MILLER, LEE OSKAR and HOWARD SCOTT

© 2000 Livingsting Music and Far-Out Music Inc, USA

Warner/Chappell North America Ltd, London W6 8BS and Universal Music Publishing Ltd, London W6 8JA

back be-fore she turn in-to a kil-la. Best for you the si-tu-a-tion not to call the bean-er. To be a true
be by you it not that com-plex. See-in' is be-liev-in' so you bet-ter change your specs. You know she not

play-er have to know how to play. If she say you're not, con-vince her, say you're gay. Nev-er ad-
gonna be wor-ry-ing 'bout things from the past, hard-ly rec-oll-ecting and then she'll go to noon-time mass. Rik boy, your

-mit to a word when she say makes a claim and you tell her ba - by no way.
ans - wer, go ov - er there. If she pack a gun ya know ya bet-ter run fast.

But she caught me on the coun-ter. It was-n't me. Saw me kiss-in' on the so-fa. It was-n't

JUST A LITTLE

Words and Music by MICHELLE ESCOFFERY,
JOHN HAMMOND-HAGAN and
GEORGE HAMMOND-HAGAN

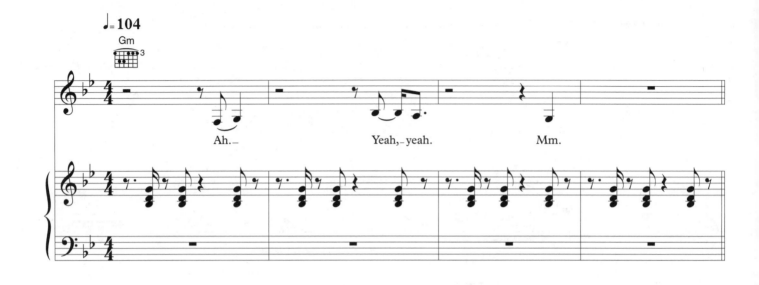

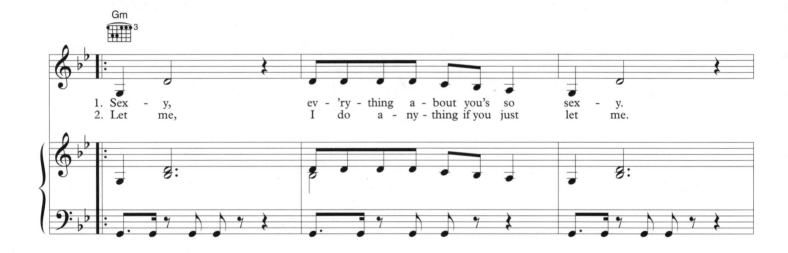

© 2002 EMI Music Publishing Ltd, London WC2H 0QY and Big Life Music Ltd, London NW1 1HY

LIFE IS A ROLLERCOASTER

Words and Music by RICK NOWELS
and GREGG ALEXANDER

© 2000 Future Furniture Music, Grosse Pointe Harlem Publishing and Keeping It Real How About You Music Publishing, USA
EMI Music Publishing Ltd, London WC2H 0QY and Warner/Chappell Music Publishing Ltd, London W6 8BS

JUST LIKE A PILL

Words and Music by ALECIA MOORE and DALLAS AUSTIN

© 2001 Pink Panther Music and Cyptron Music, USA
EMI Music Publishing Ltd, London WC2H 0QY

LET LOVE BE YOUR ENERGY

Words and Music by ROBERT WILLIAMS
and GUY CHAMBERS

© 2000 EMI Virgin Music Ltd, London WC2H 0QY and BMG Music Publishing Ltd, London SW6 3JW

when your love shines down on me.

If you're will-ing to change the world, let love be your en - er-gy,

I can't con-tain how I feel when your love shines down on me.

(Let love be your energy.)   (Let love be your energy.)

LIKE I LOVE YOU

Words and Music by CHAD HUGO,
PHARRELL WILLIAMS and JUSTIN TIMBERLAKE

© 2002 Chase Chad Music, Waters Of Nazareth Publishing and Tennman Tunes, USA
EMI Music Publishing Ltd, London WC2H 0QY and Zomba Music Publishers Ltd, London NW6 6RJ

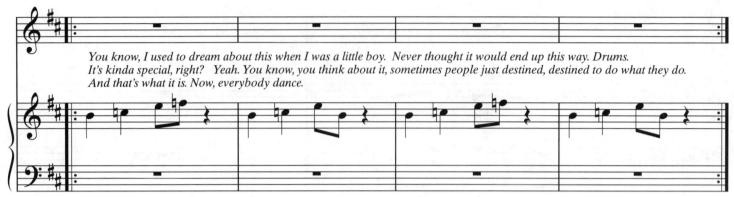

N.C.

Repeat ad lib. and fade

You know, I used to dream about this when I was a little boy. Never thought it would end up this way. Drums.
It's kinda special, right?   Yeah. You know, you think about it, sometimes people just destined, destined to do what they do.
And that's what it is. Now, everybody dance.

Verse 2:
Some people are so phony,
Nosy, 'cause they're lonely.
Aren't you sick of the same thing?
They say, so-and-so is dating,
Love you or they're hating,
When it doesn't matter anyway,
'Cause we're here tonight.
(To Pre-chorus:)

Rap:
Ma', whatcha wanna do?
I'm in front of you.
Grab a friend, see
I can have fun with two
Or me and you, put on a stage show.
In the mall, kids ask how the chain glow.
Point to her, say, wow, it's the same glow.
Point to me, I say, yeah, it's the same dough.
We're the same type, you're my a-alike.
You have me sleeping in the same bed every night.
Go ride with me, you're deserving the best.
Take a few shots, let it burn in your chest.
We could ride 'round pumpin' N.E.R.D. in the deck.
Funny how a few words turned into sex.
Play number 3, joint called "Brain." (I just love your brain.)
Ma' took her hand, made me swerve in the lane.
The name Malicious and I burn every track.
Clipse and J. Timberlake, now how heavy is that?
(To Bridge:)

MURDER ON THE DANCEFLOOR

Words and Music by GREGG ALEXANDER
and SOPHIE ELLIS-BEXTOR

© 2001 Keeping It Real How Bout You Music Publishing and Rondor Music (London) Ltd
Warner/Chappell Music Publishing Ltd, London W6 8BS and Rondor Music (London) Ltd, London W6 8JA

225

LOVIN' EACH DAY

Words and Music by RICK NOWELS and GREGG ALEXANDER

© 2000 Future Furniture Music, Grosse Pointe Harlem Publishing and Keeping It Real How About You Music Publishing, USA
EMI Music Publishing Ltd, London WC2H 0QY and Warner/Chappell Music Publishing Ltd, London W6 8BS

MUSIC

Words and Music by MIRWAIS AHMADZAÏ
and MADONNA CICCONE

Moderately fast ♩ = 120

Do you like_ to boog-ie woog-ie? Do you like_ to boog-ie woog-ie?

Do you like_ to boog-ie woog-ie? Do you like_ my ac - id rock?_

© 2000 1000 Lights Music Ltd and Webo Girl Music Publishing Inc, USA
Warner/Chappell Music Publishing Ltd, London W6 8BS and Warner/Chappell North America Ltd, London W6 8BS

omit on D.S.

Verse:

1.3. Hey, Mis-ter D J, put a rec-ord on, I wan-na dance with my ba - by._____ And when the
2. *See additional lyrics*

mu - sic starts,__ I nev - er wan-na stop, it's gon-na drive me cra - zy.

First time only

Coda

(Nev-er gon-na stop.)

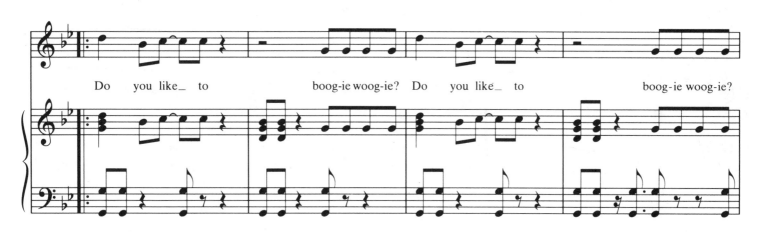

Do you like_ to boog-ie woog-ie? Do you like_ to boog-ie woog-ie?

Repeat ad lib. and fade

Do you like_ to boog-ie woog-ie? Do you like_ my ac - id rock?_

Verse 2:
Don't think of yesterday and I don't look at the clock.
I like to boogie woogie.
It's like riding on the wind and it never goes away,
Touches everything I'm in, got to have it every day.
(To Chorus:)

OUT OF REACH

Words and Music by GABRIELLE and JONATHAN SHORTEN

© 2001 Perfect Songs Ltd, London W11 1DG and Universal Music Publishing Ltd, London W6 8JA

240

OVER THE RAINBOW

Words by E Y HARBURG
Music by HAROLD ARLEN

© 1938 EMI Catalogue Partnership, EMI Feist Catalog Inc and EMI United Partnership Ltd, USA
Worldwide print rights controlled by Warner Bros Publications Inc/IMP Ltd

PAPA DON'T PREACH

Words and Music by BRIAN ELLIOT

© 1986 Elliot-Jacobsen Music Publishing Co, USA
Warner/Chappell North America Ltd, London W6 8BS

You al-ways taught_ me right_ from wrong, I need your help;_
He says that he's_ gon - na mar-ry me, we can raise_
(Instrumental)

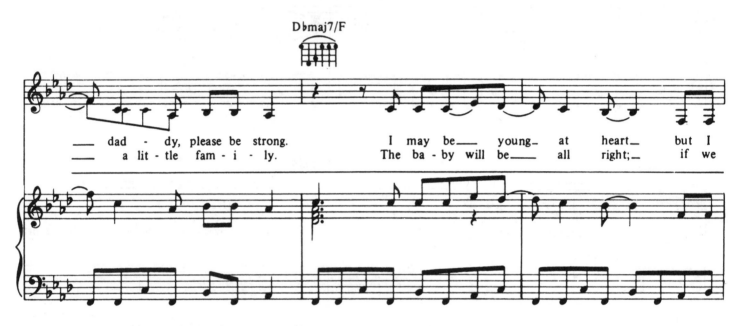

_ dad - dy, please be strong. I may be_ young_ at heart_ but I
_ a lit - tle fam - i - ly. The ba-by will be_ all right;_ if we

know what I'm say - ing. The one you warned_
sac - ri - fice. But my friends_keep tell -
Dad - dy, dad - dy if you_

PEOPLE GET READY

Words and Music by CURTIS MAYFIELD

© 1997 Mijac Music, USA
Warner/Chappell Music Ltd, London W6 8BS

QUEEN OF MY HEART

Words and Music by JOHN McLAUGHLIN,
STEPHEN ROBSON, STEVE MAC
and WAYNE HECTOR

© 2001 Windswept Pacific Music Ltd, London W6 9BD, Universal Music Publishing Ltd, London W6 8JA,
Rokstone Music Ltd, London SW6 4TJ and Rondor Music (London) Ltd, London W6 8JA

258

ROCK DA BOAT

Words and Music by RAPTURE STEWART,
ERIC SEATS and STEPHEN GARRETT

Moderately slow groove

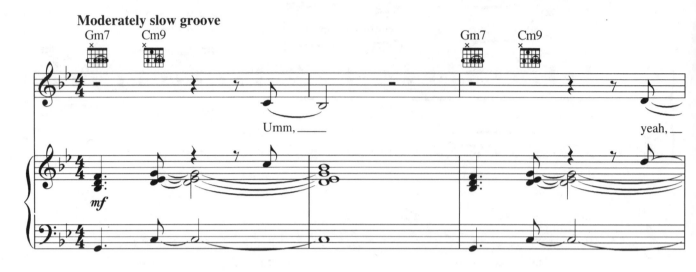

Umm, _____ yeah, _____

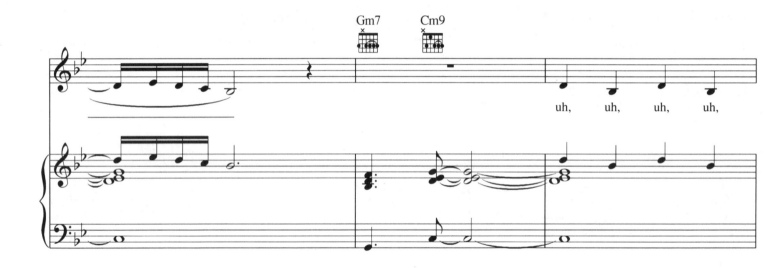

uh, uh, uh, uh,

umm _____ umm, umm, _____ yeah! _____ Boy you know you make me

© 2001 Rap Tracks Publishing, E Beats Music, Herbilicious Music and Black Fountain Music, USA
Warner/Chappell North America Ltd, London W6 8BS and EMI Music Publishing Ltd, London WC2H 0QY

ROUND ROUND

Words and Music by BRIAN HIGGINS, TIMOTHY POWELL,
MIRANDA COOPER, LISA COWLING, FELIX STRECHER,
ROBIN HOFFMAN, RINO SPADAVECCHIA, FLORIAN PFLEUGER,
KEISHA BUCHANAN, MUTYA BUENA, HEIDI RANGE and NICK COLER

Medium driving pop tempo ($\quarternote$=130)

Round, round, ba-by, round, round, spinn-ing out on me. I don't need no man, got my kicks for free. And we'll ride, stir-fried on the beat down low.

© 2002 Xenomania Music, Warner/Chappell Music Publishing Ltd, Universal Music Publishing Ltd and EMI Music Publishing Ltd
Warner/Chappell Music Ltd, London W6 8BS, Warner/Chappell Music Publishing Ltd, London W6 8BS,
Universal Music Publishing Ltd, London W6 8JA and EMI Music Publishing Ltd, London WC2H 0QY

SHE BANGS

Words and Music by WALTER AFANASIEFF,
DESMOND CHILD and IAN BLAKE

© 2000 Wally World Music, Desmundo Music, USA and A Phantom Vox Publishing, Netherlands
Sony/ATV Music Publishing Ltd, London W1V 2LP, Universal Music Publishing Ltd, London W6 8JA
and Warner/Chappell Artemis Music Ltd, London W6 8BS

SK8ER BOI!

Words and Music by LAUREN CHRISTY,
DAVID ALSPACH, GRAHAM EDWARDS
and AVRIL LAVIGNE

© 2002 Rainbow Fish Music, Ferry Hill Songs, Mr Spock Music and Almo-Music Corp, USA
Warner/Chappell North America Ltd, London W6 8BS and Rondor Music (London) Ltd, London W6 8JA

SOMETHING TO TALK ABOUT

Words and Music by DAMON GOUGH

© 2002 Badly Drawn Boy Music
Big Life Music Ltd, London NW1 1HY

Verse 3:
I've been dreaming
Of the things I learned about a boy
Who's leaving nothing else to chance again
You've got to let me in
Or let me out.

Ooh, something to talk about *etc.*

SORRY SEEMS TO BE THE HARDEST WORD

Music by ELTON JOHN
Words by BERNIE TAUPIN

© 1976 Big Pig Music Ltd, London W6 8BS

SPIRIT IN THE SKY

Words and Music by NORMAN GREENBAUM

© 1970 Great Honesty Music Inc, USA
Warner/Chappell North America Ltd, London W6 8BS

SOUND OF THE UNDERGROUND

Words and Music by BRIAN HIGGINS,
NIARA SCARLETT and MIRANDA COOPER

© 2002 Xenomania Music Ltd
Warner/Chappell Music Publishing Ltd, London W6 8BS

on in - side my mind. Don't know what, it's push-ing me high - er.

It's the sta - tic from the floor be - low. And then it drops and

catch-es like fire, it's a sound I It's a sound I It's the

know. sound of the un - der - ground. The beat of the drum goes round and a - round.

310

STRONGER

Words and Music by JONY ROCKSTAR, MARIUS DE VRIES,
FELIX HOWARD, MUTYA BUENA,
KEISHA BUCHANAN and HEIDI RANGE

1. I'll make it through the rai - ny days,— I'll be the one
2. Some-times I feel so down— and out,— like e - mo-

— who stands— here long - er than— the rest.— When my land-
-tion that's— been cap - tured in— a maze.— I had my

© 2002 Sony Music Publishing (UK), London W1V 2LP, Chrysalis Music Ltd, London W10 6SP,
Universal Music Publishing Ltd, London W6 8JA and EMI Music Publishing Ltd, London WC2H 0QY

THANK YOU

Words and Music by DIDO ARMSTRONG
and PAUL HERMAN

© 1997 Warner/Chappell Music Ltd, London W6 8BS and Cheeky Music Ltd, London NW10 4TE

SUNRISE

Words and Music by DARYL HALL, JOHN OATES,
SARA ALLEN and MICK HUCKNALL

look in-to____ your eyes I____ see the sun - rise.____ The
2. Wan-der-ing____ through life, I will____ love come home to you? And the

light be-hind____ your face helps____ me re-al-ize.____ (Sun - - - rise.____
love you want for ev - er, will they be true to you?_

© 2003 Unichappell Music Inc, Hot Cha Music Co, Fust Buzza Music, USA, and EMI Songs Ltd
Warner/Chappell Music Ltd, London W6 8BS, Rondor Music (London) Ltd, London W6 8JA and EMI Songs Ltd, London WC2H 0QY
[This song contains a sample from "I Can't Go For That" by Hall, Oates & Allen
© Warner/Chappell Music Ltd and Rondor Music (London) Ltd]

TEENAGE DIRTBAG

Words and Music by BRENDAN BROWN

1. Her name is No- el,____ I have a dream____ a- bout her. She rings my bell____ got gym class in half____ an ho- ur. Oh how she rocks____ in
2. Her boy-friend's a dick,____ he brings a gun____ to school and he'd sim- ply kick____ my ass if he knew____ the truth. He lives on my block____ and he
3. Man I feel like mould____ it's prom night and I am lone- ly. Lo and be- hold,____ she's walk- in' ov- er to me, this must be fake____ my

© 2000 Montauk Mantis Productions, USA
EMI Music Publishing Ltd, London WC2H 0QY

326

THERE YOU'LL BE

Words and Music by DIANE WARREN

Slowly ♩ = 69

(with pedal)

Verse:

think back on____ these times____ and the dreams we left____ be-hind,____ I'll be

showed me how____ it feels____ to feel the sky with-in____ my reach.____ And I

glad 'cuz I____ was blessed____ to get,____ to have you in my____ life.____ When I

al-ways will____ re-mem - ber all____ the strength you gave to____ me.____ Your love

© 2001 Realsongs, USA
EMI Music Publishing Ltd, London WC2H 0QY

WALKING AWAY

Words and Music by CRAIG DAVID and MARK HILL

© 1999 Windswept Pacific Music Ltd, London W6 9BD and Warner/Chappell Music Ltd, London W6 8BS

Verse 2:
Well I'm, so tired baby
Things you say, you're driving me away
Whispers in the powder room baby, don't listen to the games they play
Girl I thought you'd realise, I'm not like them other guys
Cos I say them with my own eyes, you should've been more wise, and
Well I don't wanna live my life, too many sleepless nights
Not mentioning the fights, I'm sorry to say lady.

I'm walking away *etc.*

UPTOWN GIRL

Words and Music by BILLY JOEL

© 1983 Joelsongs Ltd, USA
EMI Songs Ltd, London WC2H 0QY

WHAT IT FEELS LIKE FOR A GIRL

Words and Music by MADONNA CICCONE
and GUY SIGSWORTH

© 2000 Webo Girl Publishing Inc and Sigasong Ltd, USA

Warner/Chappell North America Ltd, London W6 8BS and Universal Music Publishing Ltd, London W6 8JA

Verse:

WHOLE AGAIN

Words and Music by STUART KERSHAW,
ANDY McCLUSKEY, BILL PADLEY
and JEREMY GODFREY

© 2000 Blue Noise Ltd, Windswept Pacific Music Ltd and Wise Buddah Music Ltd
EMI Virgin Music Ltd, London WC2H 0QY, Windswept Pacific Music Ltd, London W6 9BD
and Wise Buddah Music Ltd, London W1N 5AG

YEAR 3000

Words and Music by STEVE ROBSON,
JAMES BOURNE, MATTHEW JAY,
CHARLIE FLETCHER and MATTHEW SIMPSON

© 2002 EMI Music Publishing Ltd, London WC2H 0QY, Rondor Music (London) Ltd, London W6 8JA and Copyright Control

YEARS OF POPULAR MUSIC

9816A

Vol. 1 - 9817A

Vol. 2 - 9818A

Vol. 1 - 9819A

Vol. 2 - 9820A

Vol. 1 - 9821A

Vol. 2 - 9822A

Vol. 1 - 9823A

Vol. 2 - 9824A

Vol. 1 - 9825A

Vol. 2 - 9826A

Vol. 1 - 9827A

Vol. 2 - 9828A

Vol. 1 - 9829A

Vol. 2 - 9830A

Vol. 1 - 9831A

Vol. 2 - 9832A

9833A

IMP
International
MUSIC
Publications

IMP's Exciting New Series!

100 YEARS OF POPULAR MUSIC

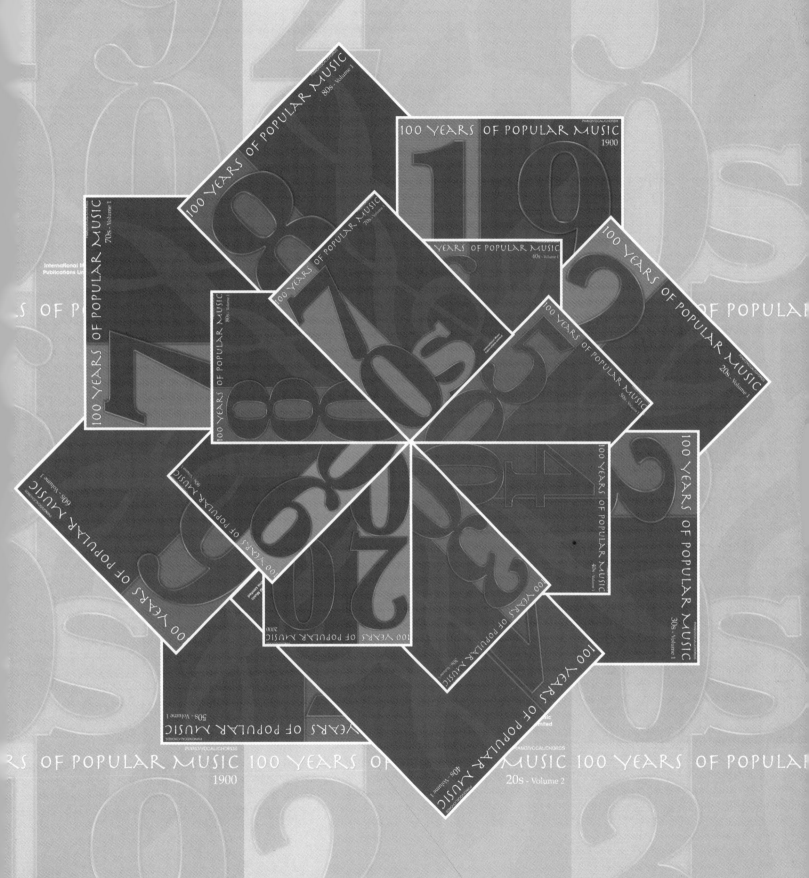

IMP
International
MUSIC
Publications

IMP's Exciting New Series!

100 YEARS OF POPULAR MUSIC

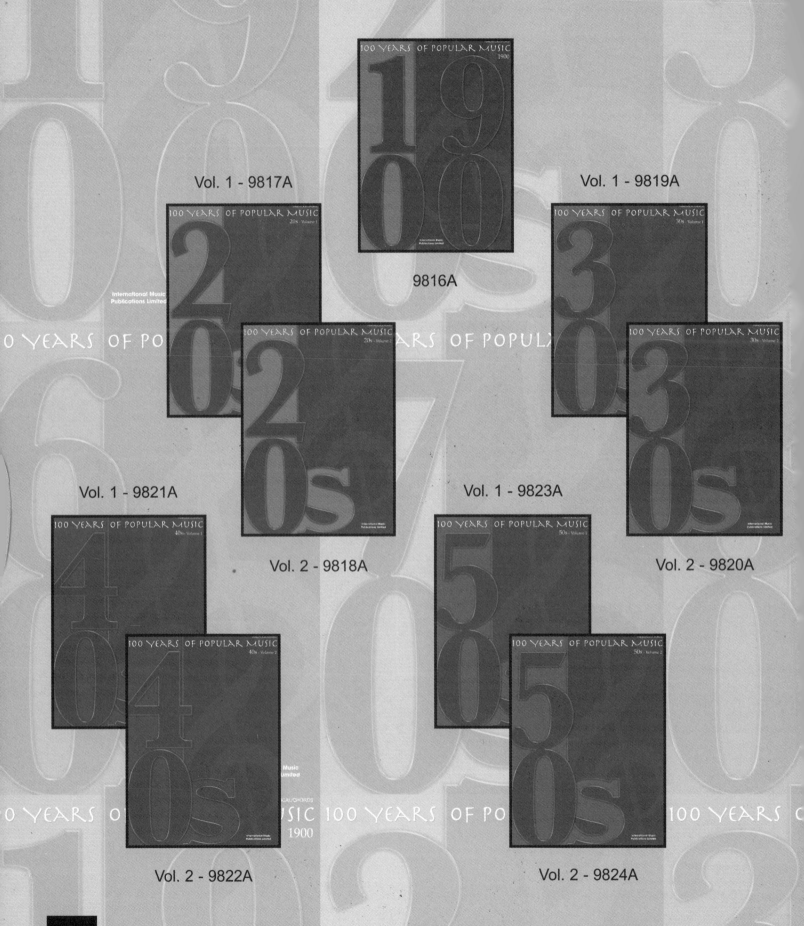

Vol. 1 - 9817A

9816A

Vol. 1 - 9819A

Vol. 1 - 9821A

Vol. 1 - 9823A

Vol. 2 - 9818A

Vol. 2 - 9820A

Vol. 2 - 9822A

Vol. 2 - 9824A

IMP
International
MUSIC
Publications

IMP's Exciting New Series!